The
Gilbert & Sullivan
Quiz and Puzzle Book

by
Nigel Bartlett

ABSON BOOKS

Abson Books   Abson   Wick   Bristol

The publishers thank Chappell Music Ltd., International Music Publications and Reginald Allen for their kind permission to reproduce the contemporary illustrations from The First Night of Gilbert & Sullivan.

Cover drawing by Bab (W.S. Gilbert) of Ko-Ko from the Mikado.

ABSON BOOKS, Abson, Wick, Bristol, England
First published in Great Britain October 1985
© Nigel Bartlett

ISBN 0 902920 64 2
Typesetting & Graphics by K.J.Studios Ltd.
Printing and binding by Burleigh Press Ltd. Bristol, England.

Introduction

The Savoy Operas, written between 1875 and 1896, were a 'hit' from their first production and have retained their popularity ever since. Gilbert's humour and satirical absurdities have an undiminished relevance to modern-day institutions and behaviour; Sullivan's gay and catchy tunes are remembered and enjoyed as most of 'pop' slides rapidly into obscurity. For these reasons the operas are still performed at professional and amateur levels and are greatly enjoyed by world-wide audiences.

How familiar are you with the operas? The puzzles and quizzes that follow have been designed to test your knowledge and there is little doubt that as you strive to recall words from the songs, the accompanying tunes will start buzzing through your head.

There are six crossword puzzles, each devoted to one of the most popular of the operas, the clues in all cases being quotations to be completed. Twelve thematic quizzes will challenge your memory of the libretti, and there are word grids, anagrams and a maze to puzzle and entertain you.

Answers to the quizzes and puzzles are to be found at the back of the book.

References to the various operas have been condensed as follows -

The Grand Duke	(GD)
The Gondoliers	(Go)
H.M.S. Pinafore	(HP)
Iolanthe	(I)
The Mikado	(M)
Patience	(Pa)
Princess Ida	(PI)
The Pirates of Penzance	(PP)
Rudigore	(R)
The Sorcerer	(S)
Trial by Jury	(T)
Utopia Ltd.	(U)
The Yeomen Of The Guard	(Y)

The texts upon which these quizzes and puzzles have been based are taken from 'The Savoy Operas' published by MacMillan.

N.B.

Manager Mr R. D'Oyly Carte.   Chef-d'Orchestre Mr Simmonds

ROYALTY THEATRE.

Dean Street   Soho.

Licensed by the Lord Chamberlain   to Miss Henrietta Hodson.

Directress

Mrs Selina Dolaro.

4

Dramatis Personae

In this grid are concealed the names of 20 Dramatis Personae. The names all consist of either one or two components, including titles, but the word 'the' is excluded. All names run in a straight line, which may read backwards or forwards, horizontally, vertically or diagonally. Letters in the grid may be used more than once, or not at all.

```
E K P G F T U S H E R I C U S
S A W I T E E N A J Y D A L A
S T R E R L C S Q I T S P C O
I I E Y O A D R S H R U T H P
L S H E S D T N X A B L A Y P
L H C D E Y R E O K O K I T O
I A N A M A R L K H C O N M O
W G A E A N A W H I P V C A H
E I L D Y G I B P S N E O N B
T W B K B E J P X A K G R J A
A D Y C U L Y E M N R Z C T H
V U D I D A Y U M Y U M O K S
I L A D Y S A N G A Z U R E F
R O L E L S I E M A Y N A R D
P R I N C E S S Z A R A N D E
```

The Gondoliers

Across

2 He led his ... from behind,
   He found it less exciting (8)

7 Or receive with ceremonial and state
   An interesting ... potentate (7)

8 Do not heed their ... surprise
   Having passed the Rubicon,
   Take a pair of rosy lips (4)

10 Now when we were ... babies
    Some one married us, that's clear (6)

11 In every doughty deed, ha, ha!
    He always took the ..., ha, ha! (4)

14 Why we bind you into posies
    ... your morning bloom has fled (3)

15 Oh, ... to earn a nobleman's praise (5)

18 The Earl, the Marquis, and the Dook,
    The Groom, the ..., and the Cook (6)

19 When, to ... Destruction's hand,
    To hide they all proceeded (5)

21 When the warrior on duty
    Goes in search of ... and beauty (4)

22 Or we run on little ... for the Ministers
    of State (7)

Down

1 For the merriest fellows are we, tra la
   That ply on the ... sea (7)

2 Every flower is a ...
   Every goose becomes a swan (4)

3 Set aside the dull enigma,
   We shall ... it all too soon (5)

4 To ... of grosser clay, ha, ha!
   He always showed the way, ha, ha! (3)

5 Then we help a fellow-creature on his path
   With the Garter or the ... or the Bath (7)

6 When he had Rhenish wine to drink
   It made him very sad to think
   That some, at junket or at jink
   Must be content with ... (5)

9 And to that end we've ... the main,
   And don't intend to return again (7)

12 We really do not care
    A preference to ... (7)

13 At summer day's nooning,
    When ... lagooning,
    Our mandolins tuning,
    We lazily thrum (5)

The Gondoliers

Down continued

16 When hearts were twice as good as gold,
   And ... times as mellow (6)
17 The Noble Lord who ... the State (5)
20 Foundation-stone laying
   I find very paying;
   It ... a large sum to my makings (4)

Colours

1 What were the colours of the uniforms of the Dragoon Guards that were criticised by Lady Jane? (Pa)

2 And what colour would Lady Jane have preferred? (Pa)

3 What is a lady's crime that merits punishment by the Mikado of being painted with walnut juice? (M)

4 What was the colour of the beautiful robe that the Contadine expected to wear when becoming Queen? (Go)

5 What colours did the Princess think the Women of Adamant should wear with scarlet and with blue? (PI)

Complete the quotations –

6 Oh, better far to live and die
Under the brave ... flag I fly (PP)

7 They will see that I'm freely ...
In a uniform handsome and chaste (Pa)

8 Such a judge of ... ... and other kinds of pottery
From early Oriental down to modern terra-cotta-ry (Pa)

9 For the Maid was Beauty's fairest Queen,
With ... tresses, like a real Princess's (PI)

10 Thy doom is nigh, ... cheek, bright eye,
Thy knell is rung, ... lip, smooth tongue (M)

11 For the merriest fellows are we, tra la,
That ply on the ... sea, tra la (Go)

12 Though so excellently wise,
For a moment mortal be,
Deign to raise thy ... eyes,
From thy heart-drawn poesy (Pa)

Pirates of Penzance

Pairs

Can you match the men in the first column with the ladies in the second column to whom they are romantically linked in the operas?

A	Archibald Grosvenor	1	Constance
B	Capt. Fitzbattleaxe	2	Elsie Maynard
C	Col. Fairfax	3	Gianetta
D	Dr. Daly	4	Josephine
E	Florian	5	Julia Jellicoe
F	Frederic	6	Mabel
G	Giuseppe	7	Melissa
H	Ludwig	8	Patience
I	Marco	9	Phyllis
J	Ralph Rackstraw	10	Princess Zara
K	Robin Oakapple	11	Rose Maybud
L	Strephon	12	Tessa

Music

1 What surprised Lady Blanche about the three new students at Castle Adamant? (PI)

2 With what did Strephon accompany himself when he sang in court to impress the Lord Chancellor? (I)

3 How did Nanki-Poo disguise himself in order to escape from Katisha? (M)

4 Which musicians so upset Ko-Ko that 'he's got 'em on his list'? (M)

Complete the quotations -

5 When ... ...
From music stands
Played Wagner imperfectly,
I bade them go,
They didn't say no,
But off they went directly (PI)

6 And I will drown the shrieks of those that fall
With ... music, such as soldiers love (PI)

7 The silvery ...,
The melancholy ...,
Were night owl's hoot
To my low-whispered coo,
Were I thy bride (Y)

8 Wake the ... that sets us lilting,
Dance a welcome to each comer,
Day by day our year is wilting,
Sing the sunny songs of summer (U)

9 The air is charged with amatory numbers,
Soft ..., and dreamy lovers' lays (S)

10 I am a broken-hearted ...
Whose mind's aesthetic and whose tastes are pure (Pa)

11 Who is longing for the rattle
Of a complicated battle
For the rum tum tum
Of the military ... (PI)

12 And the brass will crash,
And the ... bray,
And they'll cut a dash
On their wedding day (M)

The Yeomen of the Guard

2 Groom about to be …
  In an hour on Tower Green (8)

7 When maiden loves, she mopes apart,
  As … mopes on a tree (3)

8 Brave in bearing,
  Foemen scaring,
  In their bygone days of … (6)

9 Alas! I waver to and fro!
  … danger hangs upon the deed (4)

10 I have a song to sing, O!
  Sing … your song, O! (2)

12 Upon thy …
  My loving head would rest (6)

14 He's so quaint and so terse,
  both in prose and in verse;
  … though people forgive his transgression (3)

16 Forebear, my friends, and … me this ovation,
  I have small claim to such consideration (5)

17 Come, dry these unbecoming tears,
  … joyful tidings greet thine ears (4)

21 Face, with gallant heart …
  Death in most appalling shape (8)

24 But … Jack,
  He must study the knack
  If he wants to make sure of his Jill (5)

Across continued

25 Yet all the sense
  Of eloquence
  Lies … in a maid's "Ah me" (6)

Down

1 Strange adventure! Maiden wedded
  To a … she's never seen (5)

2 To the story
  Of our glory
  Each a … contributory (4)

3 O'er London town and its golden …
  I keep my silent watch and ward (5)

4 … shall we reckon risks we run
  To save the life of such an one (3)

5 And he, in well …grave,
  Within an hour is duly laid (6)

6 … has spread her pall once more,
  And the prisoner still is free (5)

11 So she begged on her knees, with downcast …,
  For the love of the merryman, moping
  mum (4)

12 I ply my craft
  And show no fear,
  … aim my shaft
  At prince or peer (3)

The Yeomen of the Guard

Down continued

13 Now what can that have been
A … so late at night,
Enough to cause a fright (4)

15 I can … you with a quip, if I've a mind;
I can trick you into learning with a laugh (5)

17 Though your wife ran away with a soldier
that day,
And took with her your trifle of … (5)

18 The … may twist and the rack may turn,
And men may bleed and men may burn (5)

19 Oh! The tales that are narrated
Of my deeds of derring-do
Have been … exaggerated (4)

20. When a wooer
Goes a-wooing
Naught is truer
Than his … (3)

22. It's a song of a merryman, moping mum
Whose soul was …, and whose glance was
glum (3)

23 But ours … not the hearts that quail,
The hands that shrink, the cheeks that
pale (3)

Anagrams

The first eight anagrams are of Dramatis Personae. Numbers 9 to 12 are of Alternative Titles of Savoy Operas. Can you solve them?

1 ADMIRES FIT BIRDS

2 RECENT FOLIO PAGES

3 I SEND A CRISP

4 ALL GREY MEN REST

5 LURING BAND THERE ON

6 THEN NOT ARM POLICE FORCE

7 DOOM ANY SCENE

8 O DREAM BY US

9 LETS OFFER GROWERS HOPS

10 'A TOT' HE DULY UTTERS

11 AND AT LAST CAME

12 THERE I END THE PAPER

The Savoy Theatre, with curtain up on Act I of PATIENCE

Food

1 What is it that the Duke of Dunstable thinks is capital to have in moderation, but not to have for breakfast, dinner and tea? (Pa)

2 What bad table manners does John Wellington Wells confess he has to Lady Sangazure? (S)

3 Eat this, puff it in his face, and you'll find yourself on Ko-Ko's list. (M)

4 What marks a conspirator in the Grand Duchy of PfennigHalbpfennig? (GD)

5 What was Rose Maybud's gift for old Gaffer Gadderby? (R)

6 What did the Baroness give Rudolf, when he was feeling low and in need of a tonic? (GD)

Complete the quotations -

7 Now for the banquet we press,
Now for the eggs and the ham,
Now for the … … …,
Now for the strawberry jam (S)

8 She never spoke when her mouth was full,
Or caught bluebottles their legs to pull,
Or spilt … … on her nice new frock,
Or put white mice in the eight-day clock (P)

9 I've … and toffee, I've tea and I've coffee
Soft tommy and succulent chops (HP)

10 But the …
And the beach
They are each
Nothing to me (R)

11 Life's a pudding full of …
Care's a canker that benumbs (Go)

12 To stuff his conversation full of quibble and of quiddity
To dine on chops and … … with avidity (Pa)

London Landmarks

The ten London landmarks, listed below, are mentioned in the Savoy Operas. They are concealed in the grid, the words running horizontally, vertically or diagonally.

First find the 'Hub of Empire' and you can then follow a route that takes you past all the landmarks named, finishing where Colonel Fairfax so nearly met his fate.

Each word follows a straight line and the next word always starts from a position immediately adjacent to the last letter of the preceeding word, although it does not necessarily run in the same direction.

Landmarks - Army and Navy Stores, Belgrave Square, Chancery Lane, Old Bailey, Piccadilly, St. James Park, Sloane Square, Somerset House, Tower of London, Westminster Hall.

The anwers at the back of the book will indicate the route you should have followed.

```
T E H U B X A D D F G H Y E E
O R O T E S R E M O S E M A N
A E U S S T U W F D N I R N G
D J S N C C S Q U A R E A D X
Q S E T V E W I L L O A N E P
B P N S C N D Y R E C N A H C
C I O T A A N W T O B M V E U
J C D J X O T K I L R T Y R P
W C N A E L Y E L I A B S A R
K A O M F S G K O L D T E U W
U D L E L F R U E H O Y H Q P
N I F S S A L M W R Y P O S D
Q L O S P M X B E L G R A V E
R L R E W O T S L L A H E I S
L Y W E S T M I N S T E R O N
```

The Pirates of Penzance

Across

1 And we find the wisest thing,
  Is to slap our … and sing (6)
4 Upon my innocence you play,
  I'm not the one to … so (4)
6 Have mercy on us, hear us, … you
  slaughter (3)
7 He loves to hear the … brook a-gurgling (6)
9 Tomorrow with the anguish …
  Of falsehood unatoned,
  I lay upon my sleepless bed,
  And tossed and turned and groaned (5)
10 No, all is still … …, on hill,
  My mind is set at ease (2, 4)
11 Ah, … me not to pine
  Alone and desolate (5)
13 Mistaking my instructions, which within my
  brain did … (6)
14 Oh, blushing buds of ever-blooming beauty!
  I, sore at heart, … your kind assistance (7)
16 When the cut- … isn't occupied in crime (6)

Across continued

17 I am the very … of a modern
  Major-General (5)
18 False, unmerciful, and truthless.
  Young and tender, … and toothless (3)
19 Though you've lived twenty one years, you're
  only five and a little bit … (4)

Down

1 Away to the … world go you,
  Where pirates all are well-to-do (8)
2 River, river, little river,
  May thy loving prosper … (4)
3 Scaling rough and rugged passes,
  Climb the hardy little lasses,
  … the bright sea-shore they gain (4)
4 At last I may atone, in some slight measure,
  For the repeated acts of theft and … (7)
5 For when … with emeutes,
  And your heart is in your boots (10)

The Pirates of Penzance

Down continued

8 I answer hard acrostics, I've a pretty taste
for ... (7)

9 With base ...
You worked upon our feelings!
Revenge is sweet,
And flavours all our dealings (6)

12 These children whom you see
Are all that I can call my own.
Take them away from me
And I shall be indeed ... (5)

15 Take heart of grace,
Thy steps retrace,
... wandering one (4)

16 ... and twenty now he's rising,
And alone he's fit to fly (3)

17 If you will cast your eyes on ...,
However plain you be, I'll love you (2)

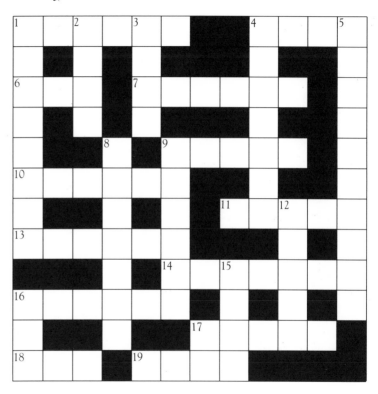

Animals

1 In Phoebe's opinion, what live animal was better than a dead lion? (Y)

2 What was it that Aline believed that the Family Sorcerer could change her into before she could turn round? (S)

3 The Queen could never understand why Iolanthe went to live amongst which creatures? (I)

4 In Lady Psyche's song, what loved a fair lady of high lineage? (PI)

5 What was Robin Oakapple's crime on Thursday? (R)

6 What was it that Colonel Fairfax assured Elsie she would resemble when curled up in Jack Point's heart? (Y)

Complete the quotations -

7 Every crevice in the keep,
Where a ... black could creep,
Every outlet, every drain,
Have we searched, but all in vain (Y)

8 Oh, happy the blossom
That blooms on the lea,
Likewise the ...
That sits on a tree (R)

9 Spit flame and fire, unholy choir!
Belch forth your venom, ... (S)

10 And Man, whose brain is to the ...
As Woman's brain to Man's (PI)

11 For, ... like, his sting lay in his tongue.
(His sting is present, though his stung is past) (PI)

12 There is eloquent outpouring
When the ... is a-roaring (M)

Snatches

The following are snatches of well-loved songs from the operas. But can you say who sings them and in which operas they occur?

1 Never mind the why and wherefore,
  Love can level ranks, and therefore

2 When I first put this uniform on,
  I said, as I looked in the glass,
  "It's one in a million
  That any civilian
  My figure and form will surpass

3 In blessings and curses
  And ever-filled purses,
  In prophecies, witches and knells

4 When I went to the Bar as a very young man,
  Said I to myself, said I

5 But I soon got tired of third-class journeys,
  And dinners of bread and water;
  So I fell in love with a rich attorney's
  Elderly, ugly daughter

6 Here's a how-de-do!
  If I marry you

7 I know a youth who loves a little maid
  Hey, but his face is a sight to see

8 It is sung to the moon
  By a love-lorn loon,
  Who fleffrom the mocking throng, O!

9 With cat-like tread,
  Upon our prey we steal,
  In silent dread
  Our cautious way we feel

10 There is beauty in the bellow of the blast,
   There is grandeur in the growling of the gale

11 I cleaned the windows and I swept the floor,
   And I polished up the handle of the big front door

12 Oh, is there not one maiden breast
   Which does not feel the moral beauty
   Of making worldly interest
   Subordinate to sense of duty

People

In which of the Savoy Operas are the following historical and legendary characters mentioned?

1 Helen of Troy

2 Bonaparte

3 James the Second

4 Caractacus

5 Lord Nelson

6 Mrs. Grundy

7 Queen Anne

8 Horace

9 Wellington

10 Hipparchus

11 King Arthur

12 Thomas Acquinas

Trial by Jury

Patience

Across

1 Tuned to each changing note,
… when he is sad (5)

3 Blind to his every mote,
… when he is glad (5)

7 Why, what a singularly … young man this
… young man must be (4)

8 Gaily pipe Pandean pleasure,
With a Daphnephoric bound,
Tread a gay but classic … (7)

10 and 5 down.
It is plain to the verriest …
That every Beauty
Will feel it her duty
To … to its glamour at once (5, 5)

11 If love is a …, how simple they
Who gather it, day by day (4)

12. When but a tiny babe of four,
Another baby played with me,
My … by a year or more (5)

15 And yet, I need not tell you why,
A tear drop … each manly eye (4)

18 A little child of beauty rare,
With marvellous … and wondrous hair (4)

20 The kettles they boiled with rage, 'tis said,
While every … went off its head (4)

Across continued

21 And who is this, whose manly face
Bears … interesting trace? (7)

23 In that case unprecedented,
… I shall live and die
I shall have to be contented
With their heartfelt sympathy (6)

24 Spreading is the figure trim!
Stouter than I used to be,
Still more corpulent … I (4)

Down

1 … is the woman's lot who, year by year,
Sees, one by one, her beauties disappear (3)

2 It cannot be joy and … deep,
Or why do these gentle ladies weep? (7)

3 Of course you will pooh-pooh whatever's fresh
and new, and declare it's crude and … (4)

4 Reduced, with …, lip-salve, and pearly grey,
To 'make-up' for lost time as best she may (5)

5 See 10 across

6 A … of Lord Waterford, reckless and rollicky
Swagger of Roderick, heading his clan (5)

9 Take of these … all that is fusible,
Melt them down in a pipkin or crucible (8)

Patience

Down continued

11 They cannot have led you
   To hang or behead you,
   Nor may they all … you,
   Unfortunate one (3)

13 Gentle sir, although to marry I …
   As yet I do not know you, and so I must
   decline (6)

14 … and Yellow! Primary colours!
   Oh! South Kensington! (3)

16 I hear the soft note of the …ing voice
   Of an old, old love, long dead (4)

17 I do not care for dirty greens
   By any means
   I do not long for all one …
   That's Japanese (4)

19 We're not quite sure if all we do has the Early
   English ring;
   But, as far as we can judge, it's something like
   this … of thing (4)

21 Though everywhere true love I …
   A-coming to all, but not to me (3)

22 If there be pardon in your breast
   For this poor penitent,
   …, with remorseful thought opprest,
   Sincerely doth repent (3)

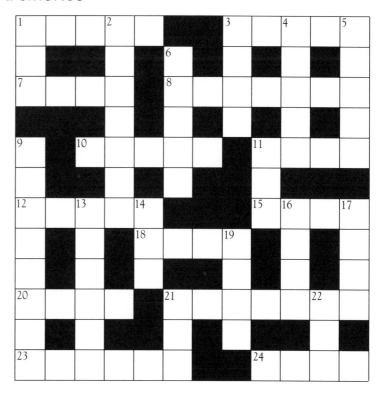

Clothing

1 What was the garment of a beautiful blue possessed by a judge? (T)

2 According to Ludwig, a lot of what was displayed in a performance of Dithyramb? (GD)

3 What was quite transparent in design, enough to make Ludwig draw the line? (GD)

4 What did Hilarion and friends don as disguise? (PI)

Complete the quotations -

5 For they hadn't mackintoshes or umbrellas or
…
And a shower with their dresses must have
played the very deuce (GD)

6 Cheap … and ties of gaudy hue,
And Waterbury watches too (GD)

7 He bought … …, and he bought dress suits,
He crammed his feet into bright tight boots (PI)

8 Every day, as the days roll on,
… … we gaily don (R)

9 You can't get high Aesthetic tastes, like …
ready made (Pa)

10 They never take off their … because
Their nails are not presentable (GD)

Maze

To lead you through this maze is a model character from one of the Operas, together with four of his ladies, relatively speaking. Follow them and you will arrive at the exit of the maze, but do not be led astray by strangers to the Operas whom you may encounter on the way.

Drink

1 In order to commit his daily crime, what does Adam advise Robin to do to Rose and Richard? (R)

2 What does Sir Despard advise Mad Margaret, when acting as District Visitor, to give to the poor? (R)

Complete the quotations -

3 I've treacle and toffee, I've ... and I've coffee
Soft tommy and succulent chops (HP)

4 None so knowing as he
At brewing a ... ... (S)

5 Pour, oh, pour the pirate ...;
Fill, oh, fill the pirate glass (PP)

6 While the pastrycook plant ... ... will grant,
Apple puffs, and three-corners, and Banburys (I)

7 For Gamma lay the costliest banquet out
For Gamma place ... ... and dry bread (PI)

8 Now for the ... of our host,
Now for the rollicking bun,
Now for the muffin and toast,
Now for the gay Sally Lunn (S)

9 The cost we may safely ignore
For the wine doesn't cost us a penny,
Tho' it's ... seventy-four (GD)

10 I weigh out tea and sugar with precision mathematical
Instead of ..., a penny each,
my orders are emphatical (GD)

Iolanthe

H.M.S. *Pinafore*

Across

2   A bud of … beauty,
    For whom proud nobles sigh (8)

7   See 19 down

8   Confide in me, fear not, I am a … (6)

9   For the union of a maiden
    With the man who … her love (4)

11 When to the ark the wearied …
    Flies from the empty waste of waters (3)

12 To his humble wail
    The echoing … replied.
    They sang "Ah, well-a-day" (5)

15 It is a … that I have composed for the use of
    the Royal Navy (4)

17 Bang-bang the loud nine-pounders … (2)

18 Carefully on … stealing,
    Breathing gently as we may (6)

20 We hope he'll find us …,
    And attentive to our duties (5)

21 In all the Royal N.
    None are so smart as … are (2)

22 Fair moon, to thee I sing,
    Bright … of the heavens (6)

25 Oh that I might retrace the … that I am
    taking (4)

Across continued

26 He never should bow down to a
    domineering frown,
    … the tang of a tyrant tongue (2)

27 She laughs my love to scorn,
    … I adore her (3)

28 Heavy the sorrow that bows the head
    When love is alive and hope is … (4)

Down

1   His energetic … should be ready to resist (4)

2   But when the … blow, I generally go
    below (7)

3   Farewell my own,
    Light of my life, farewell.
    For crime …
    I go to a dungeon cell (7)

4   Pull ashore, in fashion steady,
    … will defray the fare (5)

5   Your lordship is of opinion that married
    happiness is … inconsistent with discrepancy
    of rank (3)

H.M.S. *Pinafore*

Down continued

6 It does to a considerable extent, but it does
   not ... them as much as that (5)

10 At whose exalted ...
   A world of wealth is sighing (6)

11 Where ... yell, and clacking housewives
   fume (6)

13 ... him be shown
   At once to his dungeon cell (3)

14 ... Little Buttercup I (5)

16 Though you ... a station
   In the lower middle class (6)

18 A British ... is a soaring soul,
   As free as a mountain bird (3)

19 and 7 across.
   Sad are the sighs that ... the spell
   Uttered by eyes that ... too plainly (3, 5)

23 The ... of day, the orb of love (3)

24 Our captain, ... the day has gone
   Will be extremely down upon (3)

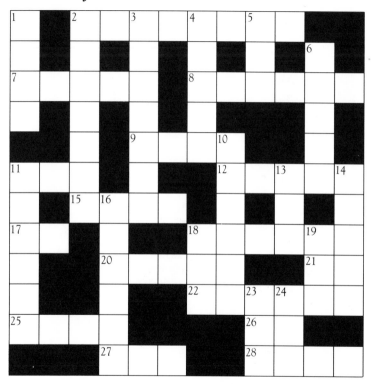

Numbers

1 At what age do girls arrive at the years of discretion in Japan? (M)

2 Sir Marmaduke's Zorah was no young beauty but was laden with the weight of how many years? (S)

3 What was the age of Iolanthe's son Strephon? (I)

4 What was the time set for the execution of Col. Fairfax? (Y)

5 At what time had Rudolph died, according to Ludwig? (GD)

6 What were the daily hours of duty of the professional bridesmaids in the village of Rederring? (R)

Complete the quotations -

7 If you are wise,
You'll shut your eyes
Till we arrive,
And not address
A lady less
Than ...-... (G)

8 Schoolgirls we, ... and under,
From scholastic trammels free (M)

9 Are you old enough to marry, do you think?
Won't you wait till you are ... in the shade? (M)

10 Hail the bride of ... summers:
In fair phrases
Hymn her praises (R)

Birds and Other Flying Creatures

Complete the quotations -

1 Things are seldom what they seem,
Skim milk masquerades as cream;
Highblows pass as patent leathers;
… strut in peacock's feathers (HP)

2 When the night wind howls in the chimney
cowls, and the … in the moonlight flies (R)

3 The … trill
Were but discordance shrill
To the soft thrill
Of wooing as I'd woo (Y)

4 She never spoke when her mouth was full,
Or caught … their legs to pull (Pa)

5 As on her nest
The tender … …
Were I thy bride (Y)

6 Cheerily carols the …
Over the cot
Merrily whistles the clerk
Scratching a blot (R)

7 Man is of no kind of use,
Man's a donkey, Man's a … (PI)

8 Braid the … hair
Weave the supple tress
Deck the maiden fair
In her loveliness (M)

9 The …
Sighed for the moon's bright ray,
And told his tail
In his own melodious way (HP)

10 And I said to him "…-…, why do you sit
Singing 'Willow, titwillow, titwillow'? (M)

Title Game

The object of this game is to fit titles of eleven of the Operas into the blank squares reading across.
Fit them into the appropriate positions and the name of a twelfth Opera will be revealed between the bold lines reading down.

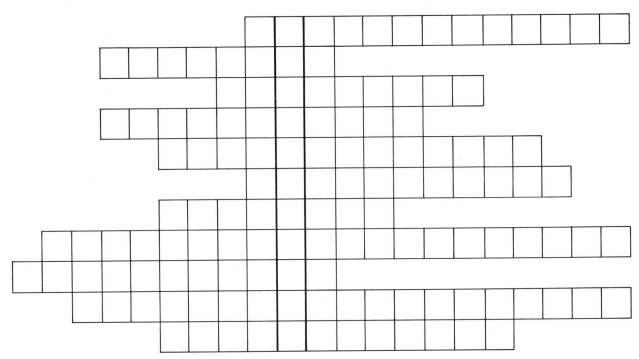

The Mikado

The Mikado

Across

1 Dye the … lip
Emphasize the grace
Of her ladyship (5)

4 And the … will crash,
And the trumpets bray (5)

7 Hearts do not break!
They sting and … (4)

9 On many a screen and fan,
We figure in lively … (5)

10 Whither, whither art thou fleeting?
Fickle moment, prithee … (4)

12 Is its beauty but a bubble
Bound to … ere long (5)

13 The sun, whose rays
Are … ablaze
With ever-living glory (3)

14 But the happiest hour a sailor sees
Is when he's down … an inland town (2)

17 What though the … may come too soon,
There's yet a month of afternoon (5)

18 To joy we soar,
Despite your scowl!
The … of our festival (6)

19 All prosy dull society sinners,
Who chatter and … and bore (5)

Across continued

21 Now every man
To aid his …
Should plot and plan (4)

23 Though I probably shall not exclaim as I …
Oh Willow (3)

24 They'd none of … be missed (2)

25 But, … and bold,
In fiery gold,
He glories all effulgent (6)

26 Gentlemen, I pray you tell me
Where a gentle … dwelleth (6)

Down

1 Then man the …, off we go,
As the fiddler swings us round (7)

2 Why, who is this whose evil eyes
… blight on our festivities (4)

3 Sooner, …, over all?
Sing a merry madrigal (5)

4 And we wonder, how we wonder
What on earth the world can … (2)

5 and 11
… and nature, thus …,
Go to make a pretty bride (3, 6)

The Mikado

Down continued

6 Two little maids remain, and they
 Won't have to wait very long, they … (3)

8 A more … Mikado never
 Did in Japan exist (6)

11 See 5 down

12 Well, dear, it can't be denied that the fact
 that your husband is to be … in a month is,
 in a way, a drawback (8)

15 Little need for woeful weeping,
 … the sad sundown is near (4)

16 When hope is gone,
 Dost thou stay on?
 May not a … maiden die (7)

19 Filled to the … with girlish glee (4)

20 I shall achieve in …
 To let the punishment fit the crime (4)

22 On a … by a river a little tom-tit
 Sang "Willow" (4)

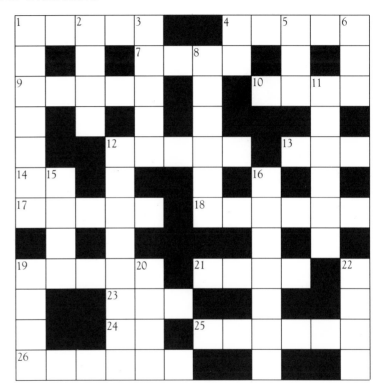

Occupations

1 Who loves to lie a-basking in the sun,
   according to a Sergeant of Police? (PP)

2 What was the occuption of Dr. Tanhauser in
   'The Grand Duke'? (GD)

3 Rose Maybud's 'Book of Etiquette' was
   composed by no less a person than the wife
   of a - ? (R)

4 Pooh-Bah is not in the habit of saying
   "How de do" to anyone under the rank of - ? (M)

Complete the quotations -

5 Away to the … we go,
   Say we're solicitous very
   Then he will turn two into one,
   Singing hey, derry down derry (R)

6 Ye well-to-do …, who live in the shires,
   Where petty distinctions are vital (R)

7 Comes a …, maybe, or a solemn D.D.
   Oh, beware of his anger provoking (Y)

8 The … in his peruke.
   The Earl, the Marquis, and the Dook (Go)

9 They're clumsy clodhoppers
   With axes and choppers,
   And shepherds and ploughmen
   And … and cowmen (R)

10 Ye supple …, who go down on your knees,
   Your precious identity sinking (R)

11 An eminent … who can make it clear to you
   That black is white, when looked at from the
   proper point of view (U)

12 A … … this, with special education,
   Which teaches what Contango means and
   also Backwardation (U)

Flowers and Trees

1 Psyche alarmed her mates at school by calling what a 'Rununculus Bulbosus'? (PI)

2 What had the power to attract Hilarion and friends when they fell over a wall? (PI)

3 Inside which flower did Iolanthe teach the Queen to curl herself? (I)

4 What kinds of flowers would mark a young man as being most particularly pure if he walked down Piccadilly with them in his hand? (Pa)

Complete the quotations -

5 Climbing over rocky mountain,
Skipping rivulet and fountain,
Passing where the ... quiver,
By the ever-rolling river (PP)

6 Pretty brook, thy dream is over,
For thy love is but a rover!
Sad the lot of ... trees,
Courted by the fickle breeze (PP)

7 You must lie upon the ... and discourse in novel phrases of your complicated state of mind (Pa)

8 Love me! I'll stick ... in my hair.
Hate me! they'll suit you not (S)

9 In a nest of weeds and nettles
Lay a ... half-hidden,
Hoping that his glance unbidden
Yet might fall upon her petals (R)

10 If love is a ... that makes you smart,
Then why do you wear it next to your heart? (Pa)

11 ... gay and hollyhock
Never shall my garden stock (PI)

12 There grew a little flower
'Neath a great ... tree;
When the tempest 'gan to lower
Little heeded she (R)

Pot Pourri

1 Which character appears in the Yeoman of The Guard but neither speaks nor sings?

2 Which is the only Savoy Opera to have a third act?

3 What 'character' sometimes appears in The Mikado purely for musical reasons, having no dramatic part?

4 In which two Operas are references made to Madame Tussaud's Waxworks?

5 A selection from which Opera was first performed at a Promenade Concert?

6 Which London Hotel had public rooms named after the G & S Operas?

7 Which was the first Opera that Queen Victoria commanded to be performed before her?

8 Which is the only Savoy Opera with no spoken dialogue?

9 What are the middle names of A.S.Sullivan and W.S.Gilbert?

10 One of the Operas had its world premiere in the U.S.A. after a single 'copyright' performance in England. Which?

11 Which was the first of the G & S Operas to be performed at the Savoy Theatre?

12 G & S were resolutely opposed to transvestism, but in one Savoy Opera men do appear in women's clothing. Which?

Answers

5 **DRAMATIS PERSONAE (horizontal)** Elsie Maynard.
Lady Jane. Lady Sangazure. Ko-Ko. Princess Zara. Ruth.
Usher. Yum-Yum. **(vertical)** Captain Corcoran.
Dick Deadeye. Katisha. Lady Angela. Lady Blanche.
Ludwig. Pooh-Bah. Private Willis. Rose Maybud
(diagonal) Pirate King. Strephon. Tessa.

6 **CROSSWORD - GONDOLIERS (across)**
2 Regiment. 7 Eastern. 8 Mild. 10 Pretty. 11 Lead.
14 Ere. 15 Sweet. 18 Butler. 19 Evade. 21 Beer.
22 Errands. **(down)** 1 Emerald. 2 Rose. 3 Guess. 4 Men.
5 Thistle. 6 Toddy. 9 Crossed. 12 Declare. 13 Weary.
16 Twenty. 17 Rules. 20 Adds.

8 **COLOURS** 1 Red and yellow. 2 Cobwebby grey.
3 Dying hair chemical yellow or puce. 4 Gold and green.
5 Crimson, violet. 6 Black. 7 Gold-laced.
8 Blue and white. 9 Golden. 10 Pink, rose. 11 Emerald.
12 Purple.

10 **PAIRS** A - 8 (Pa). B - 10 (U). C - 2 (Y). D - 1 (S).
E - 7 (PI). F - 6 (PP). G - 12 (Go). H - 5 (GD).
I - 3 (Go). J - 4 (HP). K - 11 (R). L - 9 (I).

11 **MUSIC** 1 Two were tenors, one a baritone.
2 A flagolet. 3 As second trombone. 4 Banjo serenader,
Piano-organist. 5 German Bands. 6 Trumpet. 7 Flute,
lute. 8 Lute. 9 Madrigals. 10 Troubadour. 11 Drum.
12 Trumpets.

12 **CROSSWORD - YEOMEN (across)** 2 Beheaded.
7 Owl. 8 Daring. 9 Dark. 10 Me. 12 Breast. 14 Yet.
16 Spare. 17 Most. 21 Unshaken. 24 Every. 25 Hidden.
(down) 1 Groom. 2 Bold. 3 Hoard. 4 And. 5 Earned.
6 Night. 11 Eyes. 12 But. 13 Shot. 15 Teach. 17 Money.
18 Screw. 19 Much. 20 Joy. 22 Sad. 23 Are.

14 **ANAGRAMS** 1 First Bridesmaid. 2 Sergeant of Police.
3 Princess Ida. 4 Sergeant Meryll. 5 Reginald Bunthorne.
6 The Prince Of Monte Carlo. 7 Second Yeoman.
8 Rose Maybud. 9 The Flowers Of Progress.
10 The Statutory Duel. 11 Castle Adamant.
12 The Peer And The Peri.

16 **FOOD** 1 Toffee. 2 Eats peas with a knife. 3 Peppermint.
4 Eating a sausage roll. 5 Peppermint rock. 6 A Jujube.
7 Mustard and cress. 8 Plum jam. 9 Treacle. 10 Peach.
11 Plums. 12 Roly-poly pudding.

Answers

17 **LONDON LANDMARKS** Piccadilly, Westminster Hall, Belgrave Square, Chancery Lane, Somerset House, St. James Park, Old Bailey, Sloane Square, Army and Navy Stores, Tower of London.

18 **CROSSWORD - PIRATES (across)** 1 Chests. 4 Plot. 6 Ere. 7 Little. 9 Dread. 10 In dale. 11 Leave. 13 Gyrate. 14 Implore. 16 Throat. 17 Model. 18 Old. 19 Over. **(down)** 1 Cheating. 2 Ever. 3 Till. 4 Pillage. 5 Threatened. 8 Paradox. 9 Deceit. 12. Alone. 15 Poor. 16 Two. 17 Me.

20 **ANIMALS** 1 Ass. 2 Guinea-pig. 3 Frogs. 4 Ape. 5 He shot a fox. 6 Squirrel in its nest. 7 Beetle. 8 Opossum. 9 Toads. 10 Elephant's. 11 Adder. 12 Lion.

21 **SNATCHES** 1 Capt. Corcoran, Sir Joseph Porter and Josephine (HP). 2 Col. Calverley (Pa). 3 John Wellington Wells (S). 4 Lord Chancellor (I). 5 Judge (T). 6 Yum-Yum (M). 7 Robin Oakapple (R). 8 Jack Point (Y). 9 Chorus of Pirates (PP). 10 Katisha (M). 11 Sir Joseph Porter (HP). 12 Frederic (PP).

22 **PEOPLE** 1 (S). 2 (I). 3 (T). 4 (PP). 5 (R) and (Pa). 6 (GD). 7 (Pa). 8 (R). 9 (I). 10 (PI). 11 (PP). 12 (Pa).

24 **CROSSWORD - PATIENCE (across)** 1 Sorry. 3 Merry. 7 Deep. 8 Measure. 10 Dunce. 11 Weed. 12 Elder. 15 Dews. 18 Eyes. 20 Nail. 21 Sorrows. 23 Single. 24 Grow. **(down)** 1 Sad. 2 Rapture. 3 Mean. 4 Rouge. 5 Yield. 6 Smack. 9 Elements. 11 Wed. 13 Design. 14 Red. 16 Echo. 17 Sees. 19 Sort. 21 See. 22 Who.

26 **CLOTHING** 1 Swallow-tail coat. 2 Stocking. 3 Dress of Coan Silk. 4 Lady Undergraduates' academic robes. 5 Goloshes. 6 Shoes. 7 White ties. 8 Bridesmaids' garb. 9 Trousers. 10 Gloves.

27 **MAZE** Major General Stanley, Edith, Mabel, Isabel, Kate.

28 **DRINK** 1 Poison their beer. 2 Tea and barley water. 3. Tea. 4 Jorum of tea. 5 Sherry. 6 Cherry brandy. 7 Cold water. 8 Tea. 9 Pomméry. 10 Beer.

Answers

30 CROSSWORD - PINAFORE (across) 2 Blushing.
7 Speak. 8 Mother. 9 Owns. 11 One. 12 Hills. 15 Song.
17 Go. 18 Tiptoe. 20 Clean. 21 We. 22 Regent.
25 Step. 26 Or. 27 Yet. 28 Dead. **(down)** 1 Fist.
2 Breezes. 3 Unknown. 4 Hymen. 5 Not. 6 Level.
10 Shrine. 11 Organs. 13 Let. 14 Sweet. 16 Occupy.
18 Tar. 19 Own. 23 God. 24 Ere.

32 NUMBERS 1 Fifty. 2 Fifty. 3 Twenty-four.
4 Half-past-seven. 5 Half-past-eleven. 6 Ten to four.
7 Forty-five. 8 Eighteen. 9 Eighty. 10 Seventeen.

33 BIRDS 1 Jackdaws. 2 Bat. 3 Skylark's. 4 Bluebottles.
5 Turtle dove. 6 Lark. 7 Goose. 8 Raven. 9 Nightingale.
10 Dicky-bird.

34 TITLE GAME (U), (I), (M), (PI), (Go), (T), (Pa),
(PP), (HP), (Y), (GD). Down - The Sorcerer.

36 CROSSWORD - MIKADO (across) 1 Coral. 4 Brass.
7 Ache. 9 Paint. 10 Stay. 12 Break. 13 All. 14 At.
17 Night. 18 Echoes. 19 Bleat. 21 Clan. 23 Die. 24 Em.
25 Fierce. 26 Maiden. **(down)** 1 Capstan. 2 Rain.
3 Later. 4 Be. 5 Art. 6 Say. 8 Humane. 11 Allied.
12 Beheaded. 15 Till. 16 Cheated. 19 Brim. 20 Time.
22 Tree.

38 OCCUPATIONS 1 A coster. 2 Notary. 3 Lord Mayor.
4 Stockbroker. 5 Parson. 6 Squires. 7 Bishop.
8 Chancellor. 9 Drovers. 10 M.Ps. 11 Logician.
12 Company Promotor.

39 FLOWERS AND TREES 1 Buttercup.
2 Prickly cactus. 3 Buttercup. 4 Poppy, lily. 5 Willows.
6 Poplar. 7 Daisies. 8 Sunflowers. 9 Violet. 10 Nettle.
11 Sunflower. 12 Oak.

40 POT POURRI 1 The Headsman. 2 Princess Ida.
3 Go-To who sings in the Madrigal 'Brightly dawns
our wedding day'. 4 Patience and The Mikado.
5 HMS Pinafore in 1878. 6 The Savoy.
7 The Gondoliers at Windsor Castle. 8 Trial By Jury.
9 Seymour. Schwenck. 10 The Pirates of Penzance.
11 Patience. 12 Princess Ida.

ABSON BOOKS

Other books in preparation in this Quiz and Puzzle series include: Charles Dickens, Thomas Hardy, Mrs. Gaskell and George Eliot.

Available now:-
THE JANE AUSTEN QUIZ AND PUZZLE BOOK
by Maggie Lane - £2.50
A variety of puzzles and quizzes designed to test your knowledge of Jane Austen's novels. All the answers may be found in the six novels and are included in the back of the book.

THE BRONTE SISTERS QUIZ AND PUZZLE BOOK
by Maggie Lane - £2.50
This is based on the seven novels of Charlotte, Emily and Anne with illustrations by Edmund Dulac.

THE SHAKESPEARE QUIZ AND PUZZLE BOOK
by Maggie Lane - £2.50
Illustrations by H.C. Selous
THE SHERLOCK HOLMES
QUIZ AND PUZZLE BOOK
by Nigel Bartlett - £2.50
Illustrations by Sidney Paget and Howard Elcock

LANGUAGE GLOSSARIES - 99p
RHYMING COCKNEY SLANG
SCOTTISH ENGLISH
AMERICAN ENGLISH
AUSTRALIAN ENGLISH
IRISH ENGLISH
YIDDISH ENGLISH

A full list of Abson books will be sent on request.
 All available from booksellers or by adding 25p for the first copy and 10p per copy thereafter for packing and postage from the publishers, Abson Books, Abson, Wick, Bristol BS15 5TT.